Sally and S

Written by Rozanne Lanczak Williams
Created by Sue Lewis
Illustrated by Patty Briles

Creative Teaching Press

Sally and Sammy
© 2002 Creative Teaching Press, Inc.
Written by Rozanne Lanczak Williams
Illustrated by Patty Briles
Project Manager: Sue Lewis
Project Director: Carolea Williams

Published in the United States of America by:
Creative Teaching Press, Inc.
P.O. Box 2723
Huntington Beach, CA 92647-0723

ISBN: 1-57471-864-9
CTP 3229

Sally sits on the seesaw.

Sammy sits by the sea.

Sally sits in the sandbox.

Sammy sits in a tree.

Sally sips a soda.

And Sammy sings a song.

Sally sails a sailboat.

And Sammy says, "So long."

Create your own book!

Cut a cover and inside pages for your book.
Write and illustrate things in your book that
start with the letter *s*.

I See
by
Ryan

I see a
silly seal.

Words in *Sally and Sammy*

Initial Consonant: *s*		High-Frequency Words	Other
Sally	sails	on	tree
Sammy	so	the	
sits	sailboat	by	
seesaw		in	
sea		a	
sandbox		and	
sips		long	
soda			
says			
sings			
song			